A boy called Elvis

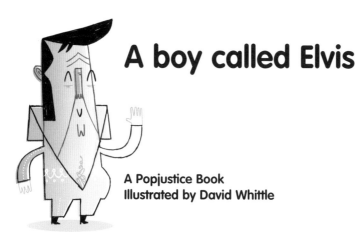

A boy called Elvis

A Popjustice Book
Illustrated by David Whittle

First published in Great Britain in 2007 by Friday Books
An imprint of The Friday Project Limited
83 Victoria Street, London SW1H 0HW

www.thefridayproject.co.uk
www.fridaybooks.co.uk

Text © Peter Robinson 2007
Illustrations © David Whittle 2007

ISBN – 13   978 1 905548 34 7

British Library Cataloguing in Publication Data

A catalogue record for this book is available
from the British Library

Designed and produced by Staziker Jones
www.stazikerjones.co.uk

The Publisher's policy is to use paper
manufactured from sustainable sources

This book belongs to

_____

I am ____ years old

My favourite Elvis song is ——————————

When I grow up, I want to be ——————————

Here is my autograph

_____

This is Elvis.

Elvis was the King of rock and roll.

Rock and roll is like pop music but a bit louder. Being the King of it means that Elvis was quite good at singing, and lots of people liked to listen to him do that.

This is different from being the King of pop. Michael Jackson is the King of pop. Michael Jackson is a different person from Elvis.

Elvis was born a very very long time ago in a place called America. His mummy made clothes and his daddy drove trucks around all day.

Elvis lived at the bottom of America. The bottom of America was a strange place in the olden days. All the people whose skin was white were very mean to people whose skin was not white.

Because it was the olden days people thought it was alright but it was not.

There was not very much money in the Elvis household.

Sometimes Elvis' mummy could only afford to give Elvis twelve burgers for dinner.

But Elvis loved his mummy, and his mummy loved Elvis. One year, for his birthday, she bought him a guitar.

She was thinking of buying him a gun but she did not. It is just as well because if Elvis was as good at shooting as he was at playing the guitar he could have killed lots and lots of people.

At school, Elvis was not very popular with girls, and his PE teacher told him off for having good hair. They used to say that he smelled.

When he was not being told off about his hair and being ignored by girls, Elvis liked to listen to music.

He liked blues music and gospel music.

Because it was the olden days, some people thought that white people were not allowed to like that music. Elvis did not worry about this because the music made him tap his toes, wiggle his hips and sing along.

Elvis liked to make songs so much that one day he went along to a recording studio where you could make your own songs if you gave them a bit of money.

Elvis handed over his money, sang some songs and came away with a shiny plastic record. He gave it to his mummy and she was very happy with it.

The songs belonged to other people but nobody minded.

The man in charge of the recording studio thought Elvis was a good singer and had an idea.

He knew that black people were singing good songs, but he also knew that white people did not like them because they were silly.

But what if a white person were to sing those songs? 'It could make a billion dollars!' said the man. Elvis sang some songs and people liked them a lot.

People found this all very confusing.

Some black people said that Elvis had just stolen their songs to make money. They were very upset.

Other black people said that if it wasn't for Elvis, nobody would have heard the songs then realised that black people's songs were actually alright.

People still argue about this today. It is a hot potato!

One day Elvis met a man called The Colonel.

The Colonel was a very important, magical man.
If he snapped his fingers, he could turn you into
a famous popstar!

'I would like to snap my fingers at you,' The Colonel
told Elvis. 'I will make you (and me) very rich.'

The Colonel's first step was to find a company who
would do more than just make one record and give
it to Elvis' mummy. He needed to find a company
who would make millions and millions of records,
then give them to teenagers.

Teenagers had not existed before Elvis came along. Before Elvis, one day you were a baby and the next thing you knew you were a grown-up.

Teenagers were invented after a big war, when mummies and daddies found that without having to buy guns and fighter planes they had some extra money in their pockets and could give it to their young boys and girls.

The boys and girls decided they would spend the money on fancy clothes, exciting haircuts and records by Elvis.

More than one million teenagers bought Elvis' first record, which was called 'Heartbreak Hotel'.

Confusingly, 'Heartbreak Hotel' was not about being in a hotel. It was about being sad about something. Elvis was singing a very clever thing called an extended metaphor, which is saying something is something when it isn't that thing. Metaphors are a minefield.

The metaphor did not really work properly because hotels always cheer you up anyway by putting a chocolate in your bed.

The Colonel was very clever. Rather than just letting teenagers buy Elvis records, he let them buy other things with Elvis' face on, too.

If teenagers wanted a salad tosser with Elvis' face on they could probably buy one!

This was very thoughtful of The Colonel and very kind to all the Elvis fans.

Whenever Elvis would sing songs on a stage, he moved his willy and bum around. Teenagers would get very excited because they had never seen anything quite like it in all their lives. Before Elvis, people had never moved their willies and bums in front of people.

Teenagers would get so excited that they would scream and run around and throw their chairs at each other. This made a real mess!

Old people sometimes got bored of having to tidy up the mess, and told Elvis to stop making teenagers so excited.

As well as singing, Elvis liked to act. The Colonel liked Elvis to act, too, and found Elvis lots of films to act in! Elvis made 27 films in ten years. Not many of them were very good.

One of the better ones was called *Jailhouse Rock*. It was all about how it is alright if you have killed someone or moved your willy and bottom with someone if they did not want you to, because if you hear some pop music you can have a dance and everything is better.

It is a shame that prisons do not use Elvis songs nowadays to make dangerous people happy. Imagine how much money prisons would save on cooking and laundry if their guests were cured by pop music.

In the olden days, you had to learn how to run around with a gun and shoot people in case there was a war and you might be useful. If you did not learn how to run around with a gun and shoot people, you were told off.

You had to go to killing school even if you were a famous popstar, so one day Elvis packed his bags and went to join the US Army.

While he was away, he met a young girl called Priscilla. Priscilla was only 14 years old and too young to kiss, so Elvis definitely did not kiss her, although he did marry her when she was old enough.

When he came back from learning how to kill, things were not always easy for Elvis. He spent a lot of time making films, which were not very good, and songs for films, which were not very good either.

People stopped liking Elvis because he was not cool any more. All the cool teenagers were more interested in running about and throwing chairs at each other at concerts by The Beatles. Elvis was an old man!

Elvis had an idea: he would make a comeback!

So, one year, just before Christmas, Elvis filmed a special TV programme.

It was called the *Elvis Comeback Special*. It was a clever name because it featured Elvis making a comeback and it was very special. Many many people watched it and suddenly people were interested in Elvis again.

Elvis bought himself some new clothes. Instead of wearing tops and bottoms, Elvis decided that it would be easier to wear one big bit of clothing, like a parachutist or a big baby.

It made going for a poo quite difficult.

One day Elvis and Priscilla decided they did not love each other very much any more. Priscilla moved out of Elvis' big house.

Elvis was very confused. He was eating lots of sweets to make him feel sleepy, so he would get a good night's sleep. Unfortunately he was still sleepy when his alarm clock went off, so he ate some more sweets to wake himself up.

He didn't know whether he was coming or going!

Munch

When Elvis was awake, he became so hungry that he could eat a whole horse in an afternoon.

He also liked to eat burgers, fries, and loaves of bread filled with peanut butter and jam.

Everyone said that Elvis was not eating healthily enough. He should have been eating a nice salad or some sticks of carrot with a nice humous dip.

But Elvis did not eat salads and humous. Silly Elvis.

One day Elvis ate so much food and so many sweets that his heart went pop.

The next day, Elvis was found on his toilet floor. He was dead.

Everybody was very upset because a bit of America had died.

A bit of America had not actually died, that is just another metaphor.

Some people think Elvis is still alive today.

Unfortunately Elvis was born so long ago that even if he were alive today he would probably be dead.

It is sad but lots of people still like to dress up as Elvis and sing his songs so even though he is not here to sing them people can still have a lot of fun.

Thankyouverymuch.

This is Elvis. Who's this with him?
It's his friend The Colonel.

Cut out around the dots (ask a grown-up to help!)
and wrap Elvis and The Colonel around your
fingers to act out special scenes!

Elvis: Thank you very much.
The Colonel: No, thank YOU very much.

Hours of fun!

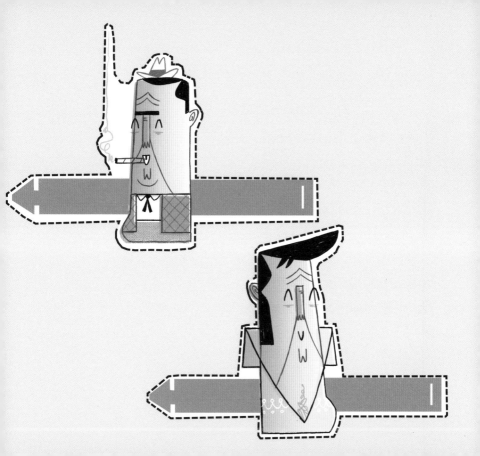

Popjustice.com is the greatest pop website on the face of Planet Earth. We update every day with the best pop stuff.

Drop in at **www.popjustice.com/idols** for downloadable wallpapers, screensavers and other random nonsense.

Why not send us an email?
idols@popjustice.com